SING-ALONG
CHRISTMAS
SONGS

Wise Publications
part of The Music Sales Group
London/New York/Paris/Sydney/Copenhagen/Berlin/Madrid/Tokyo

Published by
Wise Publications
14-15 Berners Street,
London W1T 3LJ, UK.

Exclusive Distributors:
Music Sales Limited
Distribution Centre, Newmarket Road,
Bury St Edmunds, Suffolk IP33 3YB, UK.
Music Sales Pty Limited
120 Rothschild Avenue,
Rosebery, NSW 2018,
Australia.

Order No. AM991573
ISBN 978-1-84772-234-8
This book © Copyright 2007 Wise Publications,
a division of Music Sales Limited.

Music arrangements by Jack Long and Derek Jones.
Music processed by Enigma Music Production Services and Paul Ewers Music Design.
Cover images courtesy Mark Anderson/Rubberball/Getty and iStock.
Printed in the EU.

CD tracks 1, 2, 3, 4, 5, 8, 9, 12, & 15 recorded, mixed and mastered by Jonas Persson.
Backing tracks arranged by Danny G. and John Maul.
Backing vocals by Elly Barnes.

CD tracks 6, 7, 10, 11, 13, 14, 16, 17 & 18 performed and recorded by Paul Honey and John Moores.

Your Guarantee of Quality
As publishers, we strive to produce every book
to the highest commercial standards.
This book has been carefully designed to minimise awkward
page turns and to make playing from it a real pleasure.
Particular care has been given to specifying acid-free,
neutral-sized paper made from pulps which have not been
elemental chlorine bleached. This pulp is from farmed sustainable
forests and was produced with special regard for the environment.
Throughout, the printing and binding have been planned to ensure a
sturdy, attractive publication which should give years of enjoyment.
If your copy fails to meet our high standards, please inform us and
we will gladly replace it.

www.musicsales.com

Baby, It's Cold Outside

Words & Music by Frank Loesser

Blue Christmas

Words & Music by Billy Hayes & Jay Johnson

C.H.R.I.S.T.M.A.S.

Words by Jenny Lou Carson. Music by Eddy Arnold

I'd be get-ting lots of toys that day. I learned a whole lot dif-f'rent when

Mo - ther sat me down and taught me to spell Christ - mas this

way:_____ C is for the

Christ - child,_____ born up - on this day.

T is for three wise-men, they___ who trav-elled far.

M is for the man-ger where He lay.

rall.

a tempo

A is for all He stands for,

S means shep-herds came_____ and that's why there's a

The Christmas Song
(Chestnuts Roasting On An Open Fire)

Words & Music by Mel Torme & Robert Wells

The Christmas Waltz

Words by Sammy Cahn. Music by Jule Styne

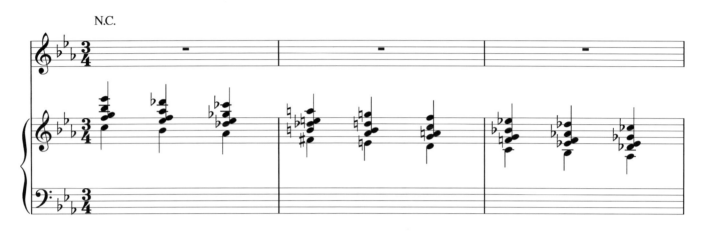

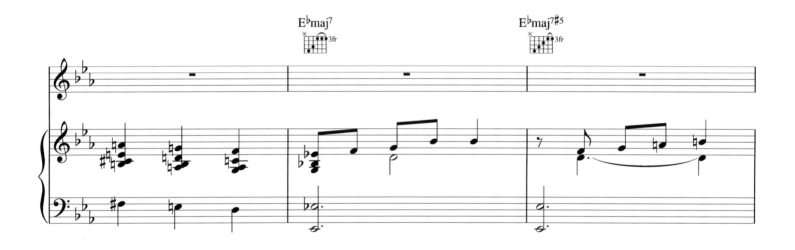

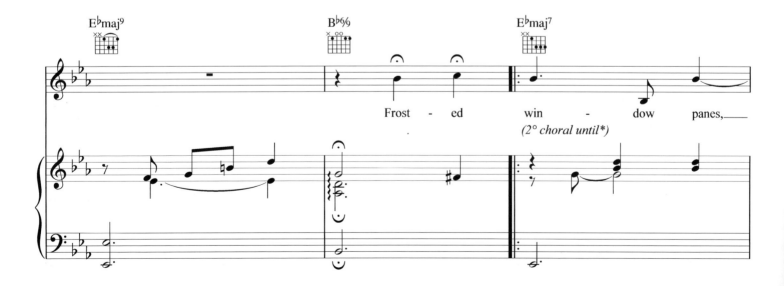

Frost - ed win - dow panes,____

(2° choral until*)

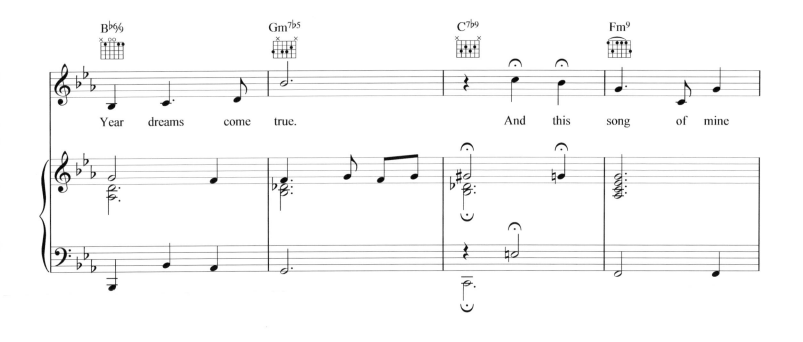

Year dreams come true. And this song of mine

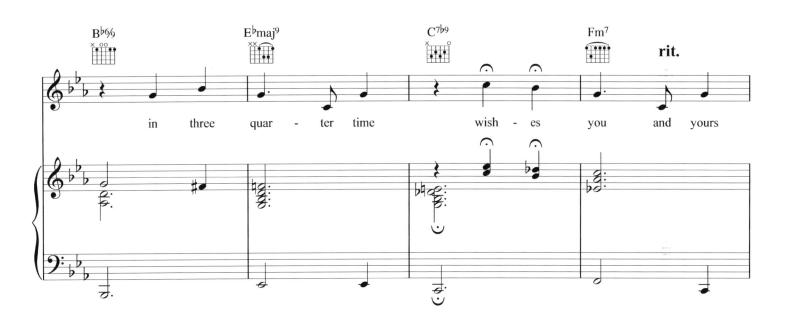

in three quar - ter time wish - es you and yours

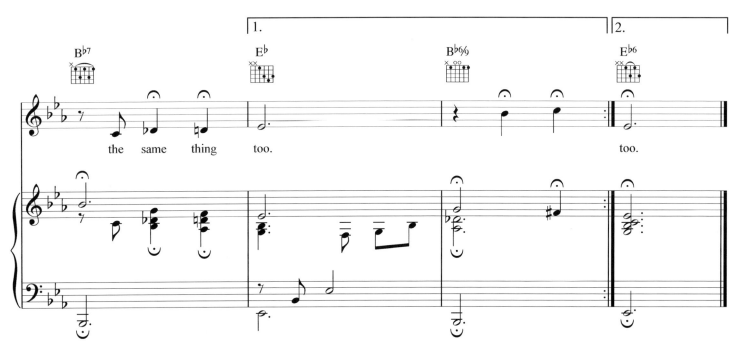

the same thing too. too.

Fairytale Of New York

Words & Music by Shane MacGowan & Jem Finer

Medium slow

(Man) 1. It was Christ - mas Eve,— babe, in the

drunk tank, when an old man said to me— "Won't see a - noth - er one". And then he

sang a song, "The rare old moun - tain dew". I turned my face a - way,— and dreamed a-

pro - mised me Broad - way was wait - ing for me._ 4. You were hand - some. *(Man)* You were pret - ty, Queen
(Verse 5 see block lyric)

of New York Ci - ty. *(Both)* When the band fin - ished play - ing, they howled out for more. Sin -

- at - ra was swing - ing; all the drunks, they were sing - ing. We kissed on the cor - ner, then

danced through the night. The boys of the N Y P D choir were sing - ing_ "Gal - way

Bay". And the bells____ were ring - ing out____ for Christ - mas Day.____

5. *(Woman)* You're a

6. *(M)* I____ could have

Verse 2:

Got on a lucky one, came in eighteen to one
I've got a feeling this year's for me and you.
So happy Christmas; I love you, baby.
I can see a better time, when all our dreams come true.

Verse 5:

(Woman) You're a bum, you're a punk!
(Man) You're an old slut on junk
Lying there almost dead on a drip in that bed!
(Woman) You scumbag! You maggot!
You cheap lousy faggot!
Happy Christmas your arse!
I pray God it's our last.

Happy Xmas (War Is Over)

Words & Music by John Lennon & Yoko Ono

Year;   let's hope it's a good one,_____ with - out an - y

fear.   3. And so this is fear.

War   is   ov - er   if   you   want   it,

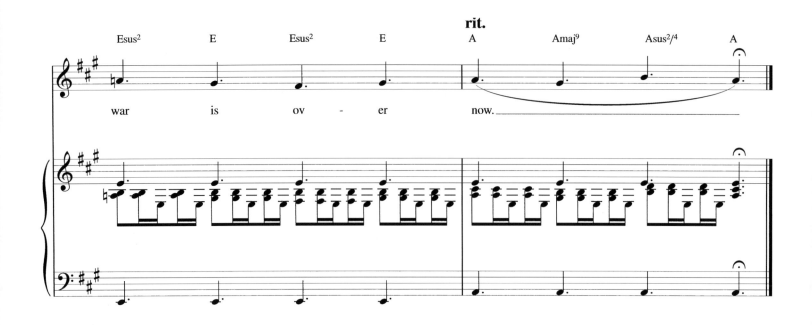

Verse 3:
And so this is Christmas, and what have we done?
Another year over, a new one just begun.
And so happy Christmas, we hope you have fun:
The near and the dear ones, the old and the young.

A very merry Christmas *etc.*

Home For The Holidays

Words & Music by Al Stillman & Robert Allen

2° A Cappella and Instrumental till *

38

no place like home for the ho - li - days

'cause no mat - ter how far a - way you

roam, if you want to be

hap - py in a mil - lion ways, for the

I Saw Mommy Kissing Santa Claus

Words & Music by Tommie Connor

It was a very strange night, I tell you, very strange!

Tap Dance

Oh yeah!

I Wish It Could Be Christmas Every Day

Words & Music by Roy Wood

on some - bo - dy's face._____ If you jump in - to your bed,___ quick - ly cov - er up___ your head;___ ___ don't you lock the doors you know that sweet San - ta Claus is on the way._____ Oh well, I wish it could be Christ -

To ⊕ Coda

52

band be-gins_ to play._____ Oh,_ I wish it could be Christ-mas_ ev-'ry day._____ So let the bells ring out for Christ-mas._____ Oh well, I

slower

Christ - mas. Why don't you give your

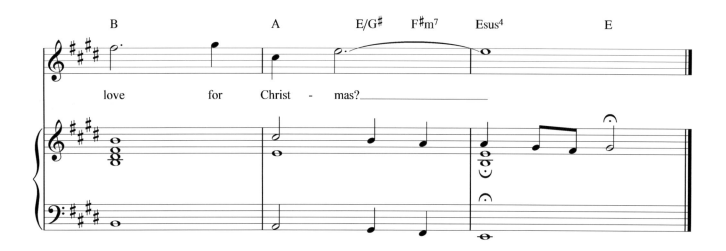

love for Christ - mas?

Verse 2:
When we're skating in the park
If the storm cloud paints it dark
Then your rosy cheeks will light my merry way.
Now the frosticles appear
And they've frozen up my beard
So we'll lie by the fire
'Til the sleep simply melts them all away.

Verse 3:
When the snowman brings the snow
Oh well, he just might like to know
He's put a great big smile on somebody's face.
So if Santa brings the sleigh
All along the Milky Way
I'll sign my name on the rooftop
In the snow then he may decide to stay.

Last Christmas

Words & Music by George Michael

Last Christ-mas I gave you my heart, but the ve-ry next day you

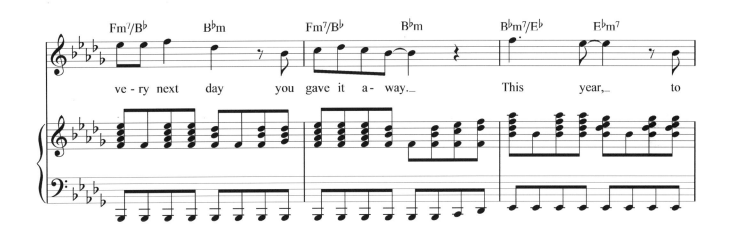

Verse 2:
A crowded room, friends with tired eyes
I'm hiding from you and your soul of ice.
My God! I thought you were someone to rely on.
Me? I guess I was a shoulder to cry on
A face on a lover with fire in his heart
A man undercover but you tore me apart...
Now I've found a real love, you'll never fool me again.

59

Let It Snow! Let It Snow! Let It Snow!

Words by Sammy Cahn. Music by Jule Styne

Lonely This Christmas

Words & Music by Mike Chapman & Nicky Chinn

lone - ly___ this Christ - mas, lone - ly___ and cold.___ It - 'll be

cold, so___ cold___ with - out you___ to hold___ this

Christ - mas.

Each time___ I re - mem - ber the day you___ went a - way,

and how I would-n't lis-ten to the things you__ had to say, I just

break down_____ as I look a-round_ and the on-ly_____ things I see are_____

emp-ti-ness_ and lone-li-ness_ and an un-lit Christ-mas tree. It-'ll be

lone-ly___ this Christ-mas with-out you__ to hold.___ It-'ll be

lone - ly___ this Christ - mas, lone - ly___ and cold.___ It - 'll be

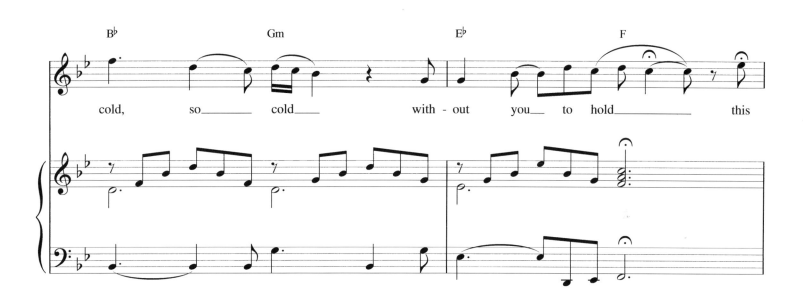

cold, so_____ cold_____ with - out you___ to hold_____ this

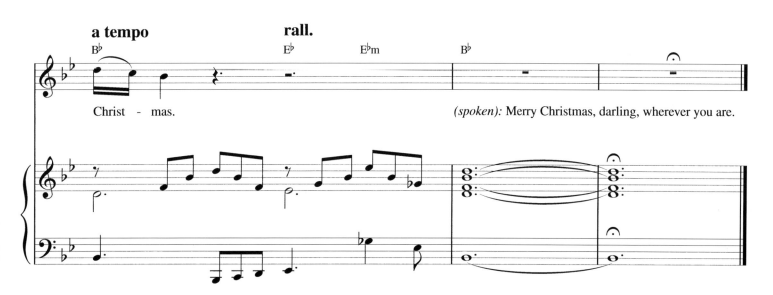

Christ - mas.

(spoken): Merry Christmas, darling, wherever you are.

Merry Xmas Everybody

Words & Music by Neville Holder & James Lea

To Coda ⊕

71

Verse 2:
Are you waiting for the family to arrive?
Are you sure you got the room to spare inside?
Does your granny always tell you, that the old songs are the best?
Then she's up and rock 'n' rolling with the best!

Verse 3:
Are you hanging up a stocking on your wall?
Are you hoping that the snow will start to fall?
Do you ride on down the hillside in a buggy you have made?
When you land upon your head, then you bin slayed!

Santa Baby

Words & Music by Joan Javits, Phil Springer & Tony Springer

Step Into Christmas

Words & Music by Elton John & Bernie Taupin

1. Wel - come to___ my christ -
(Verses 2 & 3 see block lyric)

mas song, I'd like to thank you for___ the___ year.___

Verse 2:
Take care in all you do next year
And keep smiling through the days
If we can help you, entertain you
Oh, we will find a way
So merry Christmas one and all
There's no place I'd rather be
Than asking you if you'll oblige
Stepping into Christmas with me.

Step into Christmas *etc*.

Verse 3:
As Verse 1.

Mistletoe And Wine

Words by Leslie Stewart & Jeremy Paul. Music by Keith Strachan

old has passed there's a new_____ be - gin - ning.

Dreams of San - ta, dreams of snow,

fin - gers numb, fa - ces a - glow. It's

Christ - mas time, mis - tle - toe and wine,

children singing Christian rhyme; with logs on the fire_____ and gifts on the tree, a time to re-joice in the good that we see. 2. A time_____ for liv-ing, a time for be-liev-ing; a

child - ren sing - ing Chris - ti - an rhyme; with

logs on the fire_____ and gifts on the tree, a

time to re - joice in the good that we see. 3. It's a

time_____ for giv - ing a time_____ for get - ting; a

time for for-giv-ing and for for-get-ting.

Christ-mas is love, Christ-mas is peace; a

time for hat-ing and fight-ing to cease.

Christ-mas time, mis-tle-toe and wine,

Wonderful Christmastime

Words & Music by Paul McCartney

Medium fast

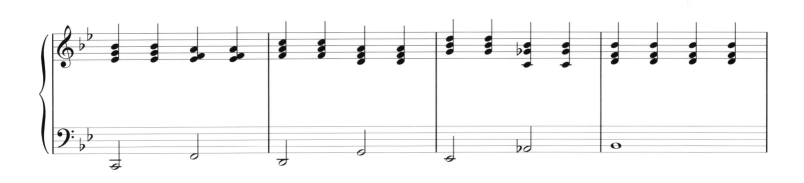

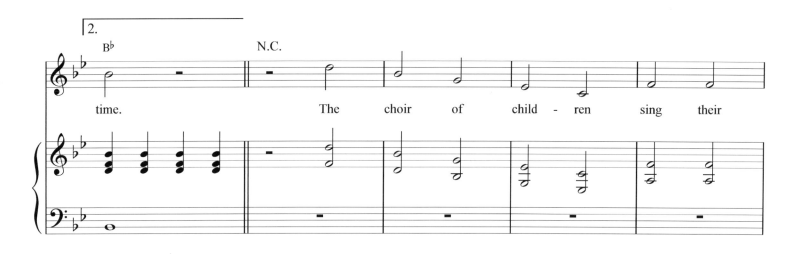

time. The choir of child - ren sing their

To ⊕ Coda

song. (𝄋 *only* They've prac - tised all year round.) Ding,

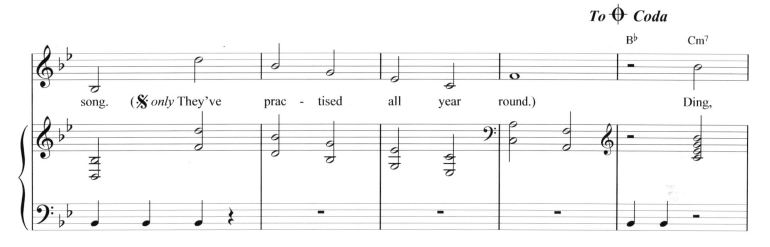

dong, ding, dong, ding, dong, ding. Ooh,____

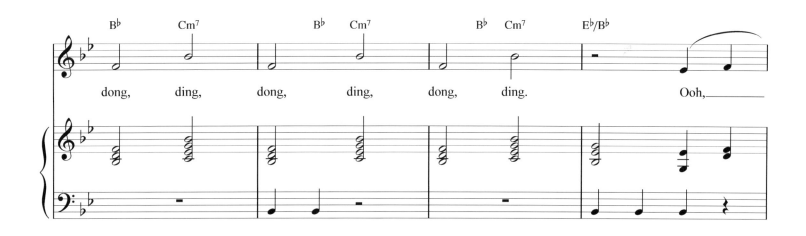

ooh.____

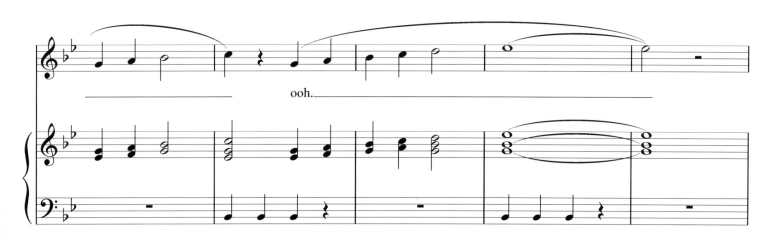

Doo, doo, doo, doo, doo doo doo.

Guitar solo

We're sim - ply hav - ing a

won - der - ful Christ - mas - time. sim - ply hav - ing a

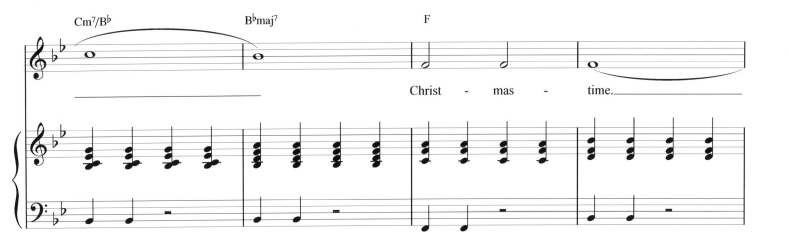

Christ - mas - time.

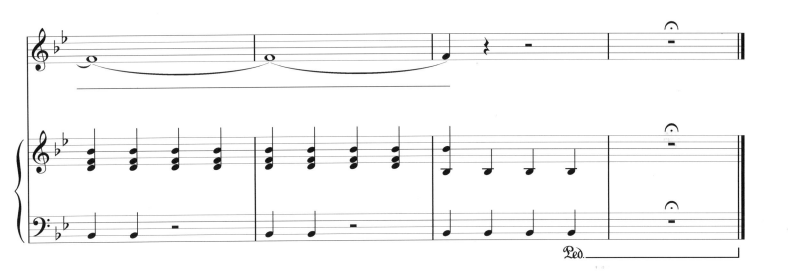

Verse 2:
The party's on, the feeling's here
That only comes this time of year.
Simply having a wonderful Christmastime.
Simply having a wonderful Christmastime.

Verse 3:
The word is out about the town
To lift a glass, oh, and don't look down.
Simply having a wonderful Christmastime.

4 5 6 7 8 9

CD Track Listing

1. Baby, It's Cold Outside
(Loesser) MPL Communications Limited.

2. Blue Christmas
(Hayes/Johnson) Anglo-Pic Music Company Limited.

3. C.H.R.I.S.T.M.A.S.
(Carson/Arnold) Carlin Music Corporation.

4. The Christmas Song
(Chestnuts Roasting On An Open Fire)
(Torme /Wells) Chappell/Morris Limited.

5. The Christmas Waltz
(Cahn/Styne) EMI Music Publishing (WP) Limited/Westminster Music Limited .

6. Fairytale Of New York
(MacGowan/Finer) BMG Music Publishing Limited/Perfect Songs Limited.

7. Happy Xmas (War Is Over)
(Lennon/Ono) Lenono Music/Ono Music.

8. Home For The Holidays
(Stillman/Allen) Edward Kassner Music Company Limited/Campbell Connelly & Company Limited.

9. I Saw Mommy Kissing Santa Claus
(Connor) Blue Ribbon Music Limited.

10. I Wish It Could Be Christmas Every Day
(Wood) Roy Wood.

11. Last Christmas
(Michael) Warner/Chappell Music Limited.

12. Let It Snow! Let It Snow! Let It Snow!
(Cahn/Styne) Warner/Chappell North America.

13. Lonely This Christmas
(Chapman/Chinn) BMG Music Publishing Limited.

14. Merry Xmas Everybody
(Holder/Lea) Barn Publishing (Slade) Limited.

15. Santa Baby
(Javits/Springer/Springer) T.M. Music Limited.

16. Step Into Christmas
(John/Taupin) Universal/Dick James Music Limited.

17. Mistletoe And Wine
(Stewart/Paul/Strachan) Patch Music Limited.

18. Wonderful Christmastime
(McCartney) MPL Communications Limited.

To remove your CD from the plastic sleeve, lift the small lip to break the perforations.
Replace the disc after use for convenient storage.